C000053961

THE GIDDY LIM!T
FIFTH ANNIVERSARY BOOK

Alex

Published by The Orcadian Limited (Kirkwall Press)
Hell's Half Acre, Hatston, Kirkwall, Orkney, KW15 1DW
Tel. 01856 879000 • Fax 01856 879001 • www.orcadian.co.uk

Text and Artwork by Alex Leonard © 2010
www.giddy-limit.com

ISBN 978-1-902957-42-5

All rights reserved. The contents of this book may not be reproduced in any form without written permission from the publishers, except for short extracts for quotation or review

Printed at The Orcadian Limited, Hatston Print Centre, Hell's Half Acre, Hatston, Kirkwall, Orkney, KW15 1DW

THE GIDDY LIMIT
FIFTH ANNIVERSARY BOOK

BY ALEX LEONARD

FOR VICKIE

INTRODUCTION

This is a remarkable Tuesday. It is deadline day and I have just finished emailing the finished artwork for the week's Giddy Limit to *The Orcadian*. It is the two-hundred and sixty-second time I have done so in the last five years and so there is nothing unusual about the day's events thus far. What makes this Tuesday remarkable however is that my next action isn't to head straight to my bed and immediately fall asleep. Instead I make a cup of tea, sit back down and stare blankly at my desk, unsure of what to do next. It is only 3.30 in the afternoon. For once I have managed to finish the strip within normal working hours. This doesn't happen often.

An unremarkable Tuesday ends up with me holed up in my little office deep into the night, finishing the week's strip sometime into the small hours (which, I concede, is technically the day after deadline day if we are being pedantic about it). As such it is usually my last conscious act before crashing lifelessly into complete and utter slumber.

The reasons for my adherence to these erratic nocturnal working patterns are partly due to the simple nature of my job, and partly self-imposed. Although many people are of the understanding that The Giddy Limit is the only work I do, the truth is that as a freelance illustrator the overwhelming majority of my work and employment comes from elsewhere, and I am happy to say keeps me in reasonably steady and sustained employment. As such, finding time to write and draw the strip each week is often a challenge as the deadline looms ever closer. If I didn't care much about the content of The Giddy Limit, and if my conscience allowed me to churn out just anything on any given week, this wouldn't really be a problem. I could make a few compromises, rush it through and move on to the next thing (or go to bed). But the truth is, I care deeply about my strip, am abundantly proud of it and am very grateful to be able to share it with the rest of Orkney each week. And so often I find myself still working and re-working the artwork or script at two or three in the morning, devoting time to it that for the most part I don't really have.

On this particular Tuesday however, things are different. As I sit here in my office exhilarated by the peculiar sensation of finishing a Giddy Limit strip under natural daylight, I begin to wonder if perhaps I have finally learned to manage my time more appropriately on what is a rather fitting anniversary: The strip that I have just completed is number two-hundred and sixty-two and so marks the dawn of the sixth year of the strip in publication. It seems a very long time ago indeed since I sent that first email off to *The Orcadian*. The strip has changed much over time and collated here in this book are the other two-hundred and sixty-one cartoons that chart the strip's development over the first five years of its life. I truly hope you enjoy them.

Alex Leonard

September 2010

IN THE BEGINNING

The Giddy Limit first appeared in *The Orcadian* in September of 2005. For perhaps ten or so years prior to this (I am not sure exactly) it existed as a nameless entity in the form of countless little sketches and scribbles in cheap sketch pads, found strewn around my university digs in Edinburgh. I think (perhaps rather indulgently) that it was on some level a metaphorical comfort blanket to me whilst away from home for the first time: I had drawn cartoons and comic books all my life, but it was seeing Orcadian dialect wrot doon oan pipper that was the final motivation for me to produce my own strip.

I am showing my age somewhat when I say that whilst at University email was really only just beginning to be widely available. I was given an email account by my university and just about the only person I knew who used email back home was my cousin (through marriage, ye pedants) Sigurd Towrie. Sigurd would always write his emails to me in dialect, and for some reason it really struck an emotional chord with me. Enthused, I started replying in dialect also. It always made me smile to try to turn

into text that which rolls so easily off the tongue. I had grown up reading Dudley D Watkins' The Broons and Oor Wullie, and was obviously a fan of R.T. Johnstone's Stenwick Days – both very strong influences to me – but this was the first time I had really tried writing in dialect myself. I liked how you heard the writing, more than you read it, and I am not ashamed to admit I found it really quite thrilling.

Like the aforementioned Oor Wullie, Bill Watterson's Calvin and Hobbes also focuses on a small boy as the main character, and is probably the greatest single influence on me in terms of becoming a cartoonist. His strip, which ended in 1995 is in my opinion still unsurpassed in terms of quality of writing and artwork. With these influences in mind, my own strip started to take shape. From its inception, the strips I started writing and drawing were almost exclusively nostalgic reconstructions of childhood memories, and so the strip being centered around a small family dynamic developed quite naturally. Everything and everyone else just sort of fell into place around it. In truth however, it was still really only a loose concept; a hobby that allowed me to reminisce about growing up in Orkney. I never truly thought it would ever develop beyond that.

And for many years to follow, it didn't. After graduating I stumbled into a career in retail management that lasted for seven years. I think perhaps only two or three times within that period I drew any cartoons. I neither thought about them, nor had the time for them. My little labour of love simply lay dormant. Then, in 2005, I took the plunge and set out to finally become a full-time freelance illustrator. My first move was to look out all my old strips, polish them up a little bit and send them off to *The Orcadian,* complete finally with a name: The Giddy Limit. I had refined the characters, understanding finally that there was a need to turn it into something long term and sustainable. James (Miller) approved it all, and kindly thought they would give it a go for – if memory serves me well – a three month trial. Finally Cheemo, Davo, Liz, Sandy and Ivy were up and running.

Much of the content of the strips that make up its inaugural year were re-draws of the ideas that I had sketched out some ten years earlier. It's astonishing to me how different these early strips look compared to those I draw now. I've never been conscious of a change in my drawing style, but it is starkly apparent when looking at these early strips. I made everything so squat, square and somewhat spiky back then. Everything is all roundy and smooth these days. (A psychiatrist would probably have a field day with that). By 2007 I had begun work on a major illustration commission that lasted until the end of the year. Consequently it became increasingly difficult for me to carve out time for the strip and so by March I had ceased to hand-letter the dialogue, opting instead to input all the text through Photoshop, which I still do to this day. It nearly halved the amount of time needed to ink each strip. Rather significantly during this period I also moved from Edinburgh back home here to Orkney. I had rather hoped that I could demonstrate how this changed the tone of the strip forever, but in truth it didn't, really. The strip was becoming more immediately topical in it's subject each week, but this owed more to my increasingly late submissions rather than my new geographical proximity.

By the third year, the content was becoming more like a diary of personal experiences than it ever was during my time living South. By comparison everything happening to me on a weekly basis – even the most nugatory of things – suddenly seemed worthy of comment. I suppose I was more confident that there was a greater authenticity to what I was writing, because it was now all based on events experienced here, at home, in Orkney. That said, this is not exclusively true of every strip in this collection: I didn't storm out in a rage from the Pier Arts Centre pavement artist competition, for example... though that was only because I was too old to enter...

THE PROCESS

Whit wey dae ye git aall yir ideas, min? is I suppose the most common question I get asked in regard to the strip. I am often tempted just to lie in order to make the process seem more celestial, because the actual truth is fairly banal. Usually, I sit at my desk on the day I have assigned myself to do the strip – usually the Tuesday – and just start thinking of potential topics. Once ideas pop up, I develop them in my head until they either reach an amusing conclusion, or become a dead end, at which point I try to think of something else. There are times when I am out and about and I'll see or hear something that I feel would make a good strip, and I'll try and make a mental note of it. The number of times I have forgotten what that idea was by the time I get back home is alarming however. (I refuse to carry around a notebook or a dictaphone though: that would place me firmly in the eccentric category, and I do not want to be found there).

As I have said previously, many of the early strips were childhood memories, but I seem to have run out of those now. The weather is always a big source of material and is always the most fun strips to draw, but I am always acutely aware that it is – as it is in conversation – the most unimaginative of topics to bring up, so I try not to write too many weather based strips too close together. I try and make the strip topical these days, or at least relevant to what has been happening around the county in that given week, as I hope it feels more like a shared experience, and something the readership can relate to. Once the idea has taken place, I begin by jotting the script down and make a decision about which characters will best act out the story. They each have a different outlook on life and so often can add an extra dimension to the idea that I may not have considered originally.

With the script more or less finalised, I sketch out the drawings, choosing to do so on rather inexpensive paper. This habit originated from my propensity to produce very detailed pencil work: I erase and re-work my pencils so often that it usually ruins the surface of decent quality paper, so I sketched on cheap stock and used a light-box to trace through on to decent paper in order to keep it clean for the inking stage. Around the first year's worth of strips were done in this fashion on to thick 300gsm watercolour paper, using a pretty heavy-duty dip pen for the inking. It is reflected in the finished artwork: it looks somewhat organic and rustic, and pretty loose in terms of detail. As I became more adept at inking, I moved to inking on 250 gsm Bristol Board which has a very smooth surface, allowing more detailed and intricate linework: again you can see the change in style as the strip moves through years two to four. Once inked, the strips were scanned, cleaned up in Photoshop and sent off to *The Orcadian*.

These days the strip has evolved further, most of the process now being done digitally on my Intuos graphics tablet, running through Photoshop. For years I consciously resisted the temptation to move towards digital illustration because I felt that there was always something more appealing about working with real materials: I love the feel of good paper, and the smell of ink and paints, and I always believed it yielded more authentic

and appealing artwork. I think it probably still does, but as I learned more about digital illustration, bought more software and hardware and learned how to use it, I started to understand its many benefits. I have had a few inking disasters over the years with spillages ruining a day's work, and it can cripple you when up against a deadline. Inking my work digitally, as I now do, you are only a click away from nullifying any mistakes. It offers such flexibility also: I can re-size or manipulate any element of the drawing at any stage, and it is quick and clean to work with. I still begin the process by sketching out my drawings and ideas on paper with a real pencil however. I'm not sure why I do, really, as it is unnecessary with all this technology at my fingertips. I suppose perhaps I still just like the feeling of paper in my hands, even if it is the pretty inexpensive stuff.

THE CHARACTERS

CHEEMO

Apparently some people are confused about the pronunciation of Cheemo's name. His name is Jeemo (as in James), but the spelling is of course a reference to our local tendency to pronounce our soft 'J' as 'Ch' (as in 'Dae ye waant cham oan yir toast?'). In fairness to those confused, it wasn't long after the strip began when I ceased to spell all 'Js' as 'Ch' in the dialogue – it was simply becoming overly confusing – so in that respect the spelling of his name is somewhat inconsistent with the rest of the strip's dialogue. By that time however it was too late to change his name, and so Cheemo he has remained.

Despite having such arduous and convoluted origins, Cheemo is actually a pretty straight forward character: He likes football, Christmas, games consoles and chips; he dislikes fetching coal, eating salad and taking baths. He is both a small version of myself now, and also a version of myself when I was small.

Cheemo primarily gets his kicks from doing the same things I used to: playing football in the garden; climbing on bales stacked in farm buildings; building go-carts and gang-huts; riding a bike; racing wooden boats down the burn and all that bruck. I acknowledge this does not make him truly representative of most children today, but in reality it would not be much fun if every week we just watched a boy sat motionless in front of a Playstation.

My girlfriend will testify to this from first-hand experience.

DAVO

Davo is the resident local farmer in the strip, and is probably the only character truly at ease with his situation. Whereas the rest of the cast seem often to be easily frustrated with island life, Davo just gets on with it. Like farmers do.

I originally set out with the idea that Davo fancied himself as an intellect and a philosopher, and that underneath it all he was really just an idiot. A few of the early strips reflect this, where he was prone to long-winded and ill-informed rants about various topics, but he quickly became repetitive and formulaic. These days he is purely an idiot.

I myself know nothing about farming. My real frame of reference for this area is my Dad and his recollections of growing up on my Grandad's farm. Consequently, Davo's milieu tends to be rather nostalgic and representative of a by-gone era of farming. This is why he shuns the more de rigueur colour-coded boiler suits of modern farming fashion etiquette in favour of old dungarees, and why he still drives a grey Fergie. The flat cap is a direct homage to my late Grandad.

Because Davo represents 'the auld days', I tend to use him as a tool with which to poke fun at the obscurities of modern life (of which – let's be honest – there are many). Bill Vaughn, the American columnist and author once described the concept of progress as "… the continuing effort to make things as good as they used to be." I've always liked that quote, and it kind of neatly sums up Davo's outlook on life.

Liz

Liz, the Mum, is the only non-Orcadian character in the strip. I've never been specific about where exactly Liz comes from, because really it's not important. What is important is that she is, by comparison, the only character looking at things from the outside in, and by default more often than not tends to act as the voice of reason in the strip.

This only became apparent to me a few months after the strip was launched, however. As with all the cast, I'd never really thought long-term about the sustainability of Liz's character; I didn't really see past the side-splitting hilarity of her not being able to understand what everyone else was saying. Once that joke had worn thin however, it was initially difficult to know what to do with her. Eventually it became apparent that her role within the strip was to lay bare the more absurd facets of life in Orkney: those that the rest of the cast are either blissfully unaware of, or choose to ignore. These days I never really think of the strip having a central character, but Liz has to date appeared in more strips than any other.

I tend to enjoy drawing Liz more than any other character because she is, by and large, the only one whose clothing varies from strip to strip. I wish I could cleverly explain what this perhaps symbolises, but in truth I don't really understand it myself. I can only hope it has nothing to do with some arcane fondness for women's clothing.

Sandy

Whereas I use the other characters as tools with which to poke fun at different aspects of life here in Orkney, Sandy – the Dad – I use primarily to mock my own peculiar habits and character flaws. Sandy is autobiographical in so much as I often portray him in situations I have found myself in, but usually his reactions in those situations better represent my more latent, true feelings. His propensity to direct verbal, damning outbursts at hapless tourists and inconsiderate road-users is probably the best illustration of this. Sandy does what I wish I had.

I have never attempted to impart what Sandy does for a living; partly because I have no idea, and partly because at this stage in the strip's life it is his role only as a Dad, husband, neighbour and customer to the other characters that is of any consequence. This may well change, however, as the strip develops and I go looking for new avenues to explore.

I grew up with several Sandys around me who were either relatives or friends of the family. My Grandad often even called me Sandy, though it was never clear if this was a clever use of the derivation of my own name (I am an Alexander), or if he was instead just confusing me with my cousin: a bonifide Sandy. I have my suspicions, though I was always rather fond of it. Thus, when it came to picking a name for my central male character, I didn't have to think for long.

Sandy sees an Orkney that is one-part real, two-parts what he wants it to be, which is, I believe, pretty much the case with anyone who is more than a little proud of where they come from.

ivy

Ivy harbours a barely-contained contempt for the public, is by nature rather terse and can be prone to erratic outbursts of casual violence; so naturally she is the local shopkeeper.

I introduced Ivy into the strip some six months after it was launched. Her overall function was to try to redress the balance of male-to-female characters, and specifically be a confidante to Liz. At the time it was proving difficult to develop Liz as a character and so I wanted someone and somewhere she could go to and better express herself. Ivy and her shop fitted the bill perfectly, and also helped better establish a feeling of 'community'. Liz has become fond of Ivy, though I think is quietly appalled by much of her opinions and actions. Ivy's intermittent encounters with Davo and their mutual love-hate relationship is always fun to write; I like how there's an implied history we can only guess at.

I love writing and drawing strips involving Ivy – she is in several ways the largest of all the characters – though she has appeared in significantly fewer strips than any other. I have a real soft spot for her, and find it very easy to forgive her aggressive and rather laconic demeanour; I spent nearly eight years working in retail management at various levels and know how soul-destroying the repetitive, cyclical nature of the industry can be. I always maintained that retail was good fun until the customers turned up.

And take it from me… they are never, ever right.

CHEEMO! LOOK AT THE STATE OF YOU! WHAT ON EARTH HAVE YOU BEEN DOING!?

NUHEEN. CHEUST PLAYIN'.

THAT'S NO **EXCUSE**! IT'S HIGH TIME YOU SORTED YOURSELF OUT! YOU CAN'T GO AROUND FOR THE REST OF YOUR LIFE LOOKING LIKE **THAT**! WHAT WOULD PEOPLE THINK!?

AYE-AYE FOLKS! WHIT'S UP THE DAY?

BEUY! IF LUKKS COULD KILL...!

ALEX

YE KEN, LIZ — AH'M RIGHT GLED WE DON'T LIVE IN A BIG CITY ANY MORE. HID WIS CHEUST TOO STRESSFUL DOON SOOTH.

UP HERE I KIN TAK' THINGS AT ME AOWN PACE. HID'S QUIET. HID'S PEACEFUL, AND AH'M IN A CONSTANT STET O' RELAXATION, YE KEN?

NO TRAFFEECK LIGHTS. NO WAN-WEY SYSTEMS... CHEUST MILE EFTER MILE O' OPEN COUNTRY ROAHDS. GETTAN' OOT-ABOOT UP HERE IS CHEUST A PLEASURE IN ITSEL'...

ALEX

GET OOT ME ROAHD YE BLINKAN' WOOLLY CRITTERS! AH'M GAAN TAE BE LETT AGAIN!

Someone actually once said this very thing to my father. I like it best when a strip writes itself.

Secretly, this is exactly what I wished would happen when I tried this as a child. I was always disappointed that it never did.

I think Adidas should look into designing a steel toe-cap boot. I have never seen a ball move as fast...

GOT YOUR WINTER WARDROBE ON AGAIN, DAVO?

MM-HMM...

HULLO IVY! AN' HOO'S ME FEVORIT LASS THE DAY?

OH LOSH, DAVO! WHIT ERE YE DIN TAE THEE **HAIR**?

AH'M PIT SOME **CHEL** IN HID... HID'S AAL PART O' ME NEW IMACH – AH'M GAAN FUR A SLIGHTLY MORE "STYLEESH" LUKK YE SEE ...

THAT WIDNO BE DIFFICULT...

AHH C'MOAN IVY... AH'M READ THE SIGNALS YER BEEN SENDIN' ME ... AH'M SEEN THE WEY YE LUKK AT ME WHEN AH'M OOT SPREADIN IN THE MEEDO ... AH'M BEEN AROOND LONG ENOUGH TAE UNDERSTAND THAT YE'VE FAALLEN FUR ME LUKKIN' THIS WEY...

I LUKK KINDO LIKE THAT CHAMES DEAN FELLAH, D'YE NO THEENK?

AYE. A REBEL WAE'OOT A CLUE ...

27

I wrote this after I, along with a handful of other passengers, once missed the train from Thurso by literally 5 seconds. I wanted to punch someone. I wrote a cartoon instead.

FITHER... YE KEN HOO SOMETIMES YE COME UP WAE AN IDEA, AN AT THE TIME HID SEEMS LIKE A GOOD IDEA, BUT EFTERWARDS YE REALISE MIBBE HID WISNA...?

AN' YE KEN HOO SOMETIMES WHEN YE TRY AN' EXPLAIN THAT TAE SOMEWAN, HID ISNA ALWIS RECEIVED THAT WEEL CAES THE SOMEWAN IS LIKELY ENGULFED WAE RAGE AT THAT POINT — AN' RATHER THAN THINK ABOOT HID AAL RATIONALLY AS THEY SHOULD — THEY GO CLEAN GYTE...?

AN' YE KEN HOO AH'M CHEUST PEEDIE...

CHEEMO! CHEUST TELL ME WHIT YE'VE — BROKKEN!

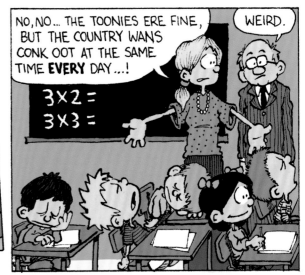

Toonies are soft. Fact.

CHEEMO? WHAT ARE **YOU** DOING UP SO EARLY? IT'S THE SCHOOL HOLIDAYS!

I KEN...

BUT YOU **HATE** IT WHEN I WAKE YOU AT THIS TIME USUALLY!

WAKIN' UP EARLY IS AOWNLY AN ISSUE IF HID'S NO YER AOWN IDEA...

GREAT... SIX WEEKS OF SMARTY-PANTS BACK-CHAT...

A CUP O' TEA WIDNO GO AMISS...

PHEW! PEAT-CUTTING SURE IS HARD WORK.

YOU WAIT TILL YE COME BACK TAE LIFT THEM...

WE HAVE TO COME **BACK**?

IN TWA WEEKS' TIME...THEN WU'LL COME BACK THE NEXT MONTH TAE TURN THEM...

THAT MEANS WE KIN COME BACK AN' STACK THEM AROOND AUGUST. HID'LL AAL BE WORTH HID COME WINTER WHEN WE COLLECT THEM OF COORSE... ...ERM... LIZ..?

AND SO I JUST PUSH A BUTTON?

...AND "POOF", INSTANT FLAMES...

SALE NOW ON

SPECIAL OFFER!
0%

This was actually one of the first strips I ever wrote, but I had to wait 10 months before I could print it in order that it coincide with Stromness Shopping Week.

THE GIDDY LIMIT

Just one year into my career as a freelance illustrator, commissions were few and far between...

There were several poignant and ardent reasons for me moving back home to Orkney, but if any were more compelling than this one, I can't remember them.

KIN YE IMAGINE WHIT HID WID BE LIKE TAE **NO** HIV THIS ON YER DOORSTEP, BEUY? 1 MEAN- NO HIVVAN SUCH BEAUTIFUL VIEWS .., NO HIVVAN THE PAECE AN' QUIET ... NO HIVVAN THIS SPACE TAE CHEUST SIT AND **THEENK** ...

MAK'S YE WINDER HOO **NORMAL** FOLK COPE.

1 KEN. MUST BE HELLEESH...

HAND IT OVER, YOUNG MAN. IT'S TOO DANGEROUS...

GET OOT O' THAT DIRTY WATTER. YE'LL **CATCH** SOMETHEEN...

COME DOON FAE THERE BEUY. HID'S NO **SAFE**.

NO CHEEMO. YOU'LL ONLY **HURT** YOURSELF.

SEE WHEN AAL THOSE TWIRNIE-FACED EENS GO OAN ABOOT HOO BAIRNS THESE DAYS SPEND TOO MUCH TIME IN FRONT O' THE T.V.? **MERCY** THAT MAKS ME MAD...

41

43

HERE YE ERE, DAVO. AH'M BOWT YE A CHRISTMAS PRESENT.

CHEERS!

NOO, IVY... DAE YOU SUBSCRIBE TAE THE IDEAL THAT HID'S REALLY THE **THOWT** THAT COUNTS?

MMM-**HMM**...

GRAND. 'CIS I **THOWT** ABOOT BUYIN YE A PRESENT... BUT I DIDNO.

ANYWAN WHO CLAIMS TAE BELIEVE IN THAT RUBBEESH IS A **LIAR**...

HEY, CHEEMO - THUR'S A FILLUM O' "**ATOMIC MAN**" ABOOT TAE START OAN THE TELLY! WAANT TAE WAATCH HID...?

NAH. I DON'T REALLY LIKE ATOMIC MAN.

EH!? I THOWT HE WIS YER FAVOURITE...!

NO, NO - HID'S "PLUTONIUM BOY" THAT I LIKE...

WE HIV A PROBLEM...

AH'VE EATEN SO MUCH DEENER THAT I KINNO MOVE ... ME PUGGY IS SO FULL O' FOOD THAT AH'M FINDIN' HID HERD TAE BREATHE ...

THE LACK O' BLOOD REACHIN' ME BRAIN IS CAUSIN' ME TEMPORARY LOSSES O' VISION ... TAE BE PERFECTLY HONEST I FEEL A BIT **SEEK**.

STICKY-TOFFEE PUDDING?

NEW YEAR'S A FUNNY AULD THING, D'YE NO THEENK? I MEAN, CELEBRATIN' SOMETHEEN THAT HISNO ACTUALLY HAPPENED YET — AND THEN ASSUMIN' THAT WHEN HID **DIS** HAPPEN, THAT HID'LL AALL BE **GOOD** — SEEMS AAFIL PRESUMPTUOUS TAE ME.

HMMM. I ALWIYS SAA HID MORE AS A CELEBRATION O' THE FACT THAT NO METTER WHIT'S GEEN OAN AFORE, WUR EACH GIVEN ANITHER CHANCE CHEUST TAE GET HID **RIGHT**.

THAT **IS** EASIER TAE DRINK TAE ...

HAPPY NEW YEAR, BEUY.

This is the only strip that has ever come close to being rejected, thought initially to be too offensive to local retailers. I guess the truth can be hurtful sometimes, but thankfully James OK'd it.

Orcadians are sublimely understated sometimes.

LUKK MITHER - AH'VE MARKED AAL O' THE THINGS IN THE CLUBBY THAT'D MAK SUITABLE BIRTHDAY PRESENTS FUR ME.

GEE THANKS.

NO BUTHER, BEUY. SO I LIKE THIS WAN, BUT IN SILVER, NO BLUE, OKAY? AN THIS IS RIGHT COOL, BUT MAKK SURE HIO'S THE **LATEST** WAN. AN' I LIKE THESE, BUT AOWNLY WAE THE OPTIONAL ROCKET LAUNCHERS.

WOULDN'T YOU RATHER GET A **SURPRISE** PRESENT? IT WON'T BE VERY EXCITING IF YOU KNOW EXACTLY WHAT YOU'RE GOING TO GET...

OAN BALANCE, HID'S PREFERABLE TAE GETTAN' SOMETHEEN **RUBBEESH** THOUGH...

The last strip I ever hand-lettered. Lordy, it used to take a long time...

I KINNO BELIEVE WIR SPENDAN' AAL THIS TIME AN' MONEY OAN **BRUKK** TAE HAND OOT TAE THE ITHER BAIRNS AT CHEEMO'S BIRTHDAY!

WHIT'S WRONG WAE A BIT O' **CAKE**? OR ICE-CREAM AND CHELLY?

DO **YOU** WANT CHEEMO TO BE KNOWN AS "THE BOY WITH THE STINGEY PARENTS"?

IF I IVVER FINND THE PARENTS WHO STERTED THIS STUPEED TRADITION - THU'LL BE GETTAN' A KEEK IN THE GOODIE BAGS FAE ME...

HEY, BUEY ... HIV YE HAERD O' **TYPOGLYCEMIA** ?

NO. WIHT IS HID ?

HID'S THE SIENFICTIC PRIPNCILE TAHT WE DNOT RAED IDNIVAIDUL LTTEERS IN A WROD, WE AONWLY RAED WRODS AS A WLOHE.

AS A REUSLT, AS LNOG AS THE FRIST AN' LSAT LTTEERS ERE IN THE RGHIT PALCE, YE KIN DAE WIHT YE WNAAT WAE THE RSET, AN' FLOK WLIL SITLL BE ELBE TAE RAED HID.

DIS HID WRIK EEVN IF YE SPEAK LKIE WE DAE ?

UKINLELY, I WID O' TOHWT ...

When I first read about this little-known anomaly I was fascinated, and was desperate to see if it applied to words written in dialect. It did. I had a lot of fun writing it.

DAE YE KEN WHIT REALLY HACKS ME OFF, BEUY ?

NO BEUY. TELL ME.

HIV YE NOTICED HOO WHEN YE WAATCH THE NEWS NOO, THEY ACTIVELY ENCOURAGE FOLK TAE "TEXT IN" THUR VIEWS OAN THE DAY'S NEWS TOPICS ... THEN THEY ACTUALLY READ THEM OOT !

I MEAN ... WHIT DAE **I** CARE WHIT "SUE" FAE "IPSWICH" THINKS ABOOT THE NEWS !? I WAANT TAE KEN WHIT THE **NEWS** FOLK THINK ABOOT THE NEWS – THAT'S WHY I PAY ME FLIPPAN' LICENSE FEE !

YOU SHOULD TEXT THUM. LET THEM KEN ...

OH, I **WILL**, BEUY. I WILL ...

I really wish I could write like this more often. One of my favourite strips.

I HEAR THEY MIGHT BE ERECTING MORE WINDMILLS AROUND HERE. I THINK IT'S GREAT... I'M ALL FOR CLEAN, SUSTAINABLE ENERGY.

AYE, BUT WU'LL AOWNLY END UP USIN' **MORE** ELECTRICITY TAE POWER AALL WUR TUMBLE DRYERS THOUGH ...

EH ? WHY ?

WANCE THOSE WINDMILLS USE UP AALL THE WIND ROOND HERE, HOO ELSE WILL WE GIT WUR WAASHEEN DRY ?

CHEEMO - HAVE YOU DONE YOUR HOMEWORK?

NOPE.

WHY NOT?

I THOWT I'D NO BUTHER WAE HID CIS AH'M NO FEELIN AALL THAT **INSPIRED** CHEUST RIGHT NOO...

OKAY, **NOO** I AM...

56

BRRIINNG-RINNG...
BRRIINNG RINNG...

...CLICK... THANK YOU FUR CAALLIN' CLARTAQUOY FARM. UNFORTUNATELY, DAVO KINNO COME TAE THE PHONE CHEUST NOO. TAE ORDER MILK OR EGGS - PRESS "WAN". TAE REPORT A BROKKEN FENCE OR A STRAY COO - PRESS "TWO". TAE COMPLAIN ABOOT A HELLEESH STINK - PRESS "THREE". FUR AALL ITHER ISSUES - PRESS "FOWER" NOO...

WU'R HIVVAN DOUBLE-PATTIE SUPPERS, LIZ... WHIT DAE YOU WAANT?

OH, I'M NOT ALL THAT HUNGRY REALLY. I'LL JUST HAVE SOME OF **YOUR** CHIPS, MAYBE...

Fish Supper.........3.50
Pattie Supper........2.20
Sausage Supper........2.20
White Pudding.........2.00
King Rib...............2.30
Chips..................1.20

I THINK THAT'S CHEUST ABOOT **THE** MOST RIDICULOUS SUGGESTION AH'VE IVVER HEARD.

TSK... **WEEMAN**.

WHIT A **STINKER** O' A DAY AH'M HIN. THIS MORNIN I GOT LINES FUR DAEIN' SOMETHEEN I DIDNO DAE ... AN' AT PLAYTIME I LOST ME FOOTBAALL OWER THE SKEUL FENCE.

THEN OAN THE BUS HOME AN AULDER BOY GAED ME THE GANGEES, AN' NOO I HIV A MILE AN' A HALF TAE WAALK HOME IN THE RAIN ...

GROWN-UPS MUST BE FORGETTAN ABOOT DAYS LIKE THESE WHEN THEY COME OOT WAE THAT "BEST YEARS O' YER LIFE" DIRT.

Gangees? Ganges? Ganjees? Who cares. It's just a funny word.

AND SO REMEMBER, CHILDREN... HERE AT SPORTS DAY – JUST AS IN LIFE – THERE ARE NO LOSERS. YOU'LL BE REWARDED SIMPLY FOR TAKING PART...

BANG!

AND IF YOU BELIEVE **THAT**, I'VE GOT A FEW OTHERS FOR YOU...

LO M8! Lng tym no C. Howz it goin. FanC a pint 2nite? i'L be n d top bar @ 7. MayB C U L8R?

WHO'S TEXTING YOU?

HID'S ME COUSEEN.

OH. AND WHAT'S HE SAYING?

AH'M SOMEWHIT ASHAMED TAE ADMIT I HIV ABSOLUTELY **NO** IDEA...

SLURRP-AAHH! THIS IS ABOOT ME FIFTH PINT O' WATTER THE DAY, LIZ. AH'M PLAYIN FOOTBAALL LATER OAN THE DAY, YE SEE ...

AND...?

WEEL, AH'M BEEN READIN' THIS BOOK OAN SPORT SCIENCE AN' AALL THAT, AN' HID SAYS THAT CHEUST A **TWO** PERCENT DROP IN YER HYDRATION LEVEL CAN LEAD TAE UP TAE A **TWENTY** PERCENT DROP IN YER PERFORMANCE LEVEL ...

I SEE... AND WHAT DID YOUR BOOK SAY ABOUT FAT BELLIES? DID IT SAY HOW MUCH FAT BELLIES AFFECT YOUR PERFORMANCE LEVEL ...?

I WAS ONLY **JOKING!**

HEY MITHER! WHIT YE DAEIN'? GET IN TAE YER COSTUME! THE PARADE'S GAAN TAE STERT SOON!

OH, CHEEMO... **COUGH!** I'M SO SORRY BUT I'M REALLY SICK... I JUST DON'T THINK I CAN TAKE YOU...

BUT YOU **PROMISED!** AH'VE BEEN WAITIN' TAE DAE THIS FUR **MONTHS!** WU'VE BEEN MAKKIN' WUR COSTUMES **AALL WEEK!** WU'R A DOUBLE-ACT! IF **YOU** DON'T COME THEN **I** CAN'T GO! HOW COULD YE **DAE** THIS TAE ME?!

WELL... WHAT DO YOU SUGGEST?

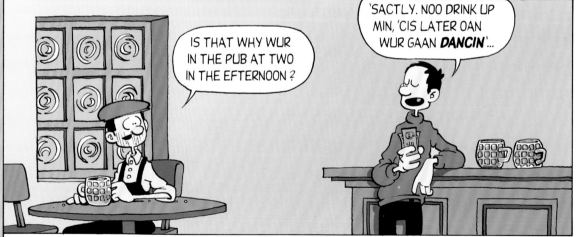

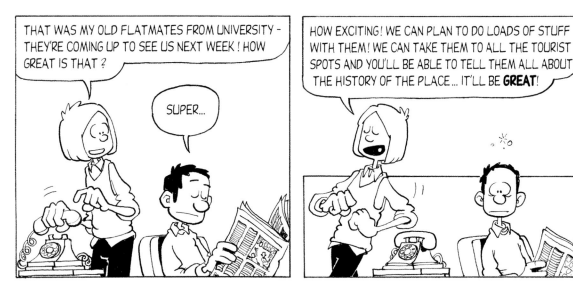

Washing your car in Orkney is one of the most futile endeavours possible.

BEUY, BEUY, BEUY... WID YE LUKK AT AALL THESE EMPTY SHOPS AT THIS END O' THE STREET NOO ... HID'S SUCH AN AAFIL SHAME DY'E NO THINK? YE KEN - WHEN I WIS PEEDIE THEY WIR AALL TRADIN' QUITE SUCCESSFULLY...

AND I MIND OAN THAT THIR AALWIS SEEMED TAE BE PLENTY FOLK OOT SHOPPIN' IN THE STREET... THE TOON FELT REALLY *VIBRANT*, YE KEN? BUT LUKK AT HID NOO. BEUY... HID BRAKKS ME HEART, LIZ, HID REALLY DIS...

JIST AS SOON AS I GIT BACK FAE THE SUPERMARKET, AH'M GAAN TAE WRITE A LETTER TAE THE PIPPER ABOOT THIS...

CAULD NOO BEUY, EH?

AYE. HID'S DEFINITELY *TURNED* INDEED.

THE NIGHTS ERE FAIR DRAAIN IN ASWEELL.

YASS. THE WINTER HAS FINALLY SET IN, I DOOT.

NO BE LONG TILL CHRISTMAS NOO...

WHY AT THIS TIME O' YEAR IS CONVERSATION REDUCED TAE JIST AN EXCHANGE O' CLICHÉS?

BIG PUDDLE AHEAD, CHEEMO BEUY!

THEN *HAAD HER CHAPPIN*, FITHER!

YEEEEHA!! WOO HOO HOO! SPLOOSH!!

BEUY, I CHEUST *NIVVER* TIRE O' DAEIN THAT...

WHIT YE DAEIN?

I'M TYPING ADDRESS LABELS FOR ALL OF THE CHRISTMAS CARDS WE SEND THIS YEAR. PRETTY GOOD, EH?

ADMITTEDLY IT'S TAKEN ME ALL DAY, BUT WE'LL NEVER HAVE TO WRITE THEM OUT EVER AGAIN. YOU SEE, ONCE I'VE PRINTED TH— FOOMP!

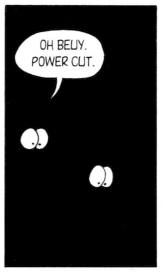

OH BEUY. POWER CUT.

DID YE CLICK 'SAVE' AT ANY POINT..?

NO.

ERE YOU GREETAN?

MM-HMM.

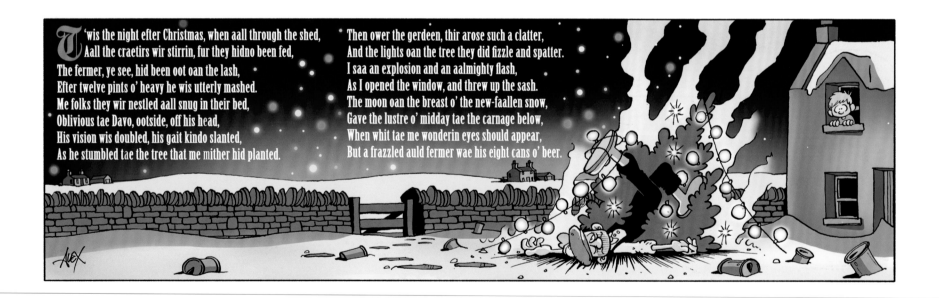

'Twis the night efter Christmas, when aall through the shed,
Aall the craetirs wir stirrin, fur they hidno been fed,
The fermer, ye see, hid been oot oan the lash,
Efter twelve pints o' heavy he wis utterly mashed.
Me folks they wir nestled aall snug in their bed,
Oblivious tae Davo, ootside, off his head,
His vision wis doubled, his gait kindo slanted,
As he stumbled tae the tree that me mither hid planted.

Then ower the gerdeen, thir arose such a clatter,
And the lights oan the tree they did fizzle and spatter.
I saa an explosion and an aalmighty flash,
As I opened the window, and threw up the sash.
The moon oan the breast o' the new-faallen snow,
Gave the lustre o' midday tae the carnage below,
When whit tae me wonderin eyes should appear,
But a frazzled auld fermer wae his eight cans o' beer.

Living in the country, and having a great view… it's only a matter of time.

The only two-part strip I have ever written. I should do more.

I was terrified of this job as a boy. I never admitted to it though.

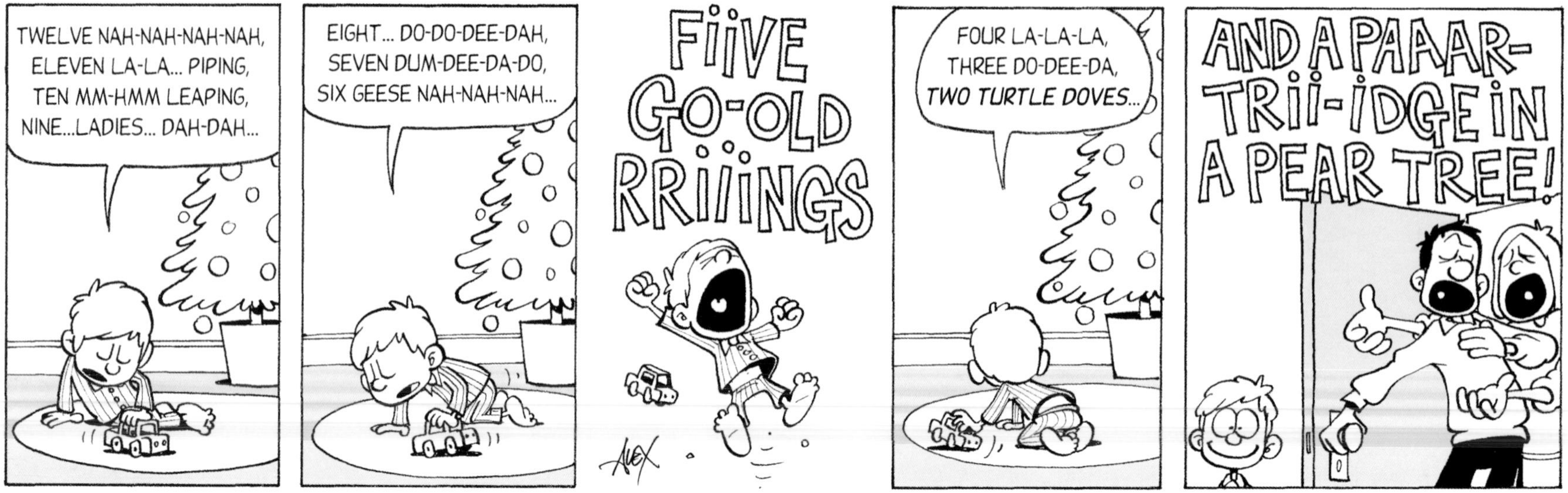

It's the only part anyone knows...

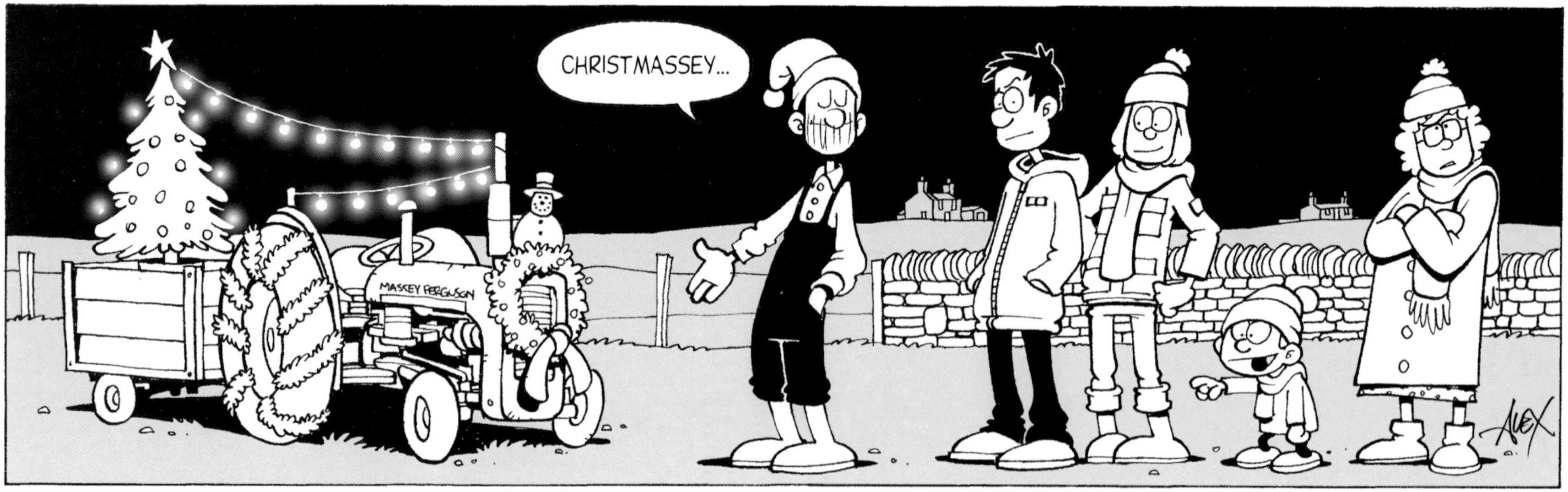

TIPEECAL! EFTER AALL THAT WAITIN' AROOND FUR SNOW, WHEN HID FINALLY ARRIVES HID'S THE WRONG **KIND**! THIS IS NO USE TAE ANYWAN!!

LUKK - HID'S TOO DRY AND POODERY! HID JIST FAALLS APART IN YIR HANDS WHEN YE TRY TAE MAKK SNOWMEN OR SNOWBAALLS OR -

FWAP!

JIST ADD WATTER... WHY DIDNO I THINK O' THAT?

YE PICK UP THESE TIPS OWER THE YEARS, BEUY...

DID YOU HEAR ABOUT THIS NEWS STORY? A TRAIN STATION DOWN SOUTH HAS BANNED PEOPLE ON PLATFORMS FROM KISSING ONE ANOTHER BECAUSE IT CAUSES OTHER PASSENGERS TO GET DELAYED.

HAVE YOU EVER HEARD ANYTHING SO **RIDICULOUS**?

I KEN. HID'S COMPLETELY OOT O' TOUCH WAE REALITY.

FOLK DON'T EVEN **WEAR** PLATFORMS THESE DAYS...

R.I.P. Woolies. Things will never be the same again.

114 footer placeholder

114

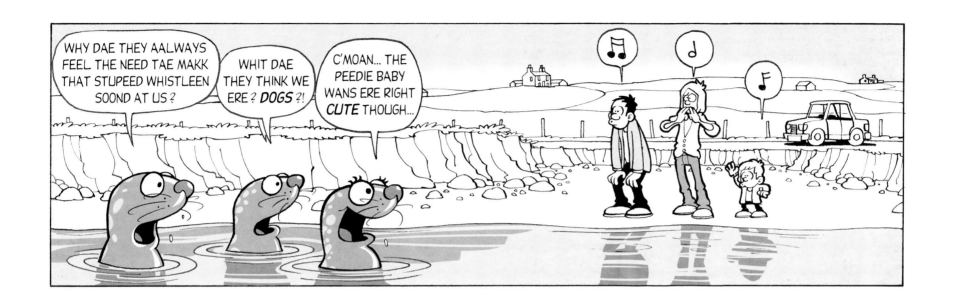

YOU'RE OPEN TWENTY-FOUR HOURS A DAY NOW? I WOULDN'T HAVE THOUGHT YOU HAVE ENOUGH CUSTOM TO DEMAND THOSE SORTS OF HOURS...

NOW OPEN 24 HRS

I DON'T. AH'M OPEN TWENTY-FOUR HOORS A *WEEK*...

NOW OPEN 24 HRS

SO THAT'S THE FOOTBAALL SEASON FEENEESHED, BEUY. YE'LL MISS HID, WILL YE?

I WILL THAT, MIN. AND WHIT A SEASON HID'S *BEEN*: SUCH DRAMA FAE STERT TAE FEENEESH! SUCH HIGHS... SUCH LOWS; THE TEARS... THE JOY...WHEN HID'S AALL OWER, HID LAEVES SUCH A SPIRITUAL VOID THAT HID'S DIFFICULT TAE IMAGINE HOO AH'LL COPE WAEOOT HID...

LITTE

THAT SAID – OAN THE UP-SIDE, I KIN NOO GET TAE THE CHIPPY EARLIER OAN A TUESDAY AND THURSDAY NIGHT...

SWEENGS AND ROONDABOOTS, BEUY...

OPEN

This strip proved to be very popular, though I have been reliably informed that wine rather than tea would have been a more appropriate indulgence.

The first strip done entirely digitally. Nobody noticed.

HERE: TAKE THIS.

WHIT IS IT?

A SMALL LIST OF SUGGESTED GIFTS WITH WHICH TO SURPRISE ME ON CHRISTMAS MORNING...

THERE HE IS... NOO: IS HE OOT O' ME RANGE? MIBBE. HID'S A TOUGH SHOT. MIBBE *TOO* TOUGH. AH'LL NO GIT ANITHER CHANCE, THOUGH: HID'S NOO OR NIVVER CHEEMO BELLY..

HEY! DROOPY DRAAERS!

SCHLAP!

HOLY MOLEY! I ACTUALLY *DID* HID! RIGHT *SMACK* IN THE MOOTH! HA HA HA! PRAISE BE! HID'S A CHRISTMAS *MIRACLE*!!

BY JINGO HID'LL BE "BOXING" DAY FUR YOU *NOO*, BELLY...

FAIR FA' YOUR HONEST, SONSIE FACE, GREAT CHIEFTAIN O THE PUDDIN'-RACE! ABOON THEM A' YE TAK YOUR PLACE, PAINCH, TRIPE, OR THAIRM: WEEL ARE YE WORDY OF A GRACE, AS LANG'S MY ARM. THE GROANING TRENCHER THERE YE FILL, YOUR HURDIES LIKE A DISTANT HILL, YOUR PIN WAD HELP TO MEND A MILL IN TIME O NEED, WHILE THRO YOUR PORES THE DEWS DISTIL, LIKE AMBER BEAD. HIS KNIFE SEE RUSTIC LABOUR DIGHT, AN CUT YOU UP WI READY SLIGHT, TRENCHING YOUR GUSHING ENTRAILS BRIGHT, LIKE ONIE...

WHIT'S *HE* OAN ABOOT?

SSSHH! HE'S ADDRESSING THE HAGGIS.

AND WHEN DIS HE BEGIN TAE ADDRESS THE ISSUE O' HOO HUNGRY WE AALL ERE?

PARISH STORES

OPEN

CLUNK!

PARISH STORES

OPEN

SHOOGLE SHOOGLE

PARISH STORE

OPEN

NRRG!

HOW LONG UNTIL HE REMEMBERS HE HAS TO PUSH?

COULD BE HOORS... DAVO BRINGS NEW MEANING TAE THE TERM "SIMPLE COUNTRY FOLK"

131

When I came up with this strip, I had confused the symbol for old pence and consequently Davo had originally paid in shillings. Only the keen eyes at *The Orcadian* editorial office saved my embarrassment. Phew.

Stromness Parish v St Andrews Parish, Market Green, 2010: It was absurd.

144